Unicorns in uniforms

Russell Punter

Illustrated by David Semple

It's opening day at the Snazzy Hotel.

The staff all look fine,
in maroon uniforms
with bright, shiny buttons.

The doorman salutes
and points to the door.

But he spins it
too quickly.

Lord Stork hits
the floor.

"I'll carry your bags, sir," the porter declares,

but he bumbles and fumbles
and they tumble downstairs.

"This way," yells the bell boy.

I'll show you your room.

Lord Stork goes to lunch.
Clumsy waiters rush by.

Watch that cucumber soup!

Lord Stork's had enough.
Then the band starts to play.

Ukuleles strum gently.
Horns honk, honk away.

Flutes toot a sweet tune.
The music's divine.

Lord Stork has a plan.
"I'll buy your hotel...

Now the Snazzy Hotel
is a huge concert hall

and its Unicorn Orchestra brings pleasure to all.

About phonics

Phonics is a method of teaching reading used extensively in today's schools. At its heart is an emphasis on identifying the *sounds* of letters, or combinations of letters, that are then put together to make words. These sounds are known as phonemes.

Starting to read
Learning to read is an important milestone for any child. The process can begin well before children start to learn letters and put them together to read words. The sooner children can discover books and enjoy stories and language, the better they will be prepared for reading themselves, first with the help of an adult and then independently.

You can find out more about phonics on the Usborne Very First Reading website, **www.usborne.com/veryfirstreading** (US readers go to **www.veryfirstreading.com**). Click on the **Parents** tab at the top of the page, then scroll down and click on **About synthetic phonics**.

Phonemic awareness

An important early stage in pre-reading and early reading is developing phonemic awareness: that is, listening out for the sounds within words. Rhymes, rhyming stories and alliteration are excellent ways of encouraging phonemic awareness.

In this story, your child will soon identify the *u* sound, as in **unicorns** and **uniforms**. Look out, too, for rhymes such as **door – floor** and **bumbles – fumbles**.

Hearing your child read

If your child is reading a story to you, don't rush to correct mistakes, but be ready to prompt or guide if he or she is struggling. Above all, do give plenty of praise and encouragement.

Edited by Jenny Tyler and Lesley Sims
Designed by Hope Reynolds

Reading consultants: Alison Kelly and Anne Washtell

First published in 2019 by Usborne Publishing Ltd., Usborne House, 83-85 Saffron Hill, London EC1N 8RT, England.
www.usborne.com Copyright © 2019 Usborne Publishing Ltd.